Backyard Friends

Backyard Friends

story and illustrations by
Linda Kennedy Sweeney

Haley's
Athol, Massachusetts

Copy edited by Debra Ellis.

Haley's

488 South Main Street

Athol, MA 01331

haley.antique@verizon.net

978.249.9400

for my husband, Ken,

and my two sons,

Timothy and Ryan,

who have encouraged me

and

who are my Number 1 fans

Late on a summer afternoon, when all is very quiet and still,

Mother Nature comes to life . . .

when the birds and squirrels come out

to play in the backyard.

Mr. Squirrel is out in the yard with his friends.

He jumps and hops around the yard searching for a treat.

Then, he stops and sits up

holding a treasure he has found buried in the ground.

He hops over to the fountain and gets a drink of water.

Then he continues on his way,

in search of more buried treasure.

Other squirrels are also having fun

playing hide-and-seek out in the yard . . .

. . . while others chase each other

around and around the trunk of a tree.

High up in the trees, another squirrel

leaps from one branch to another

on his way around the woods.

Mrs. Robin is also out in the yard searching

for a fat, juicy worm to peck out of the earth.

When she finds one,

she will bring it home

to feed her babies in their nest.

Other robins play Giant Step in the yard.

They seem to bounce along the grass.

One hop, two hops, . . .

. . . they bounce along . . .

then stop and wait to take another hop.

If it is a hot day, Mr. Robin may hop

into the bird bath to get nice and cool.

As daylight fades and the sun begins to get

lower and lower in the sky,

it is time to go home.

The squirrels and robins have had a busy day

playing and searching for treasures.

Now it is time to go to sleep . . .

. . . for tomorrow will bring another busy day of adventure.

About the Author/Illustrator

Linda Joy Kennedy Sweeney

photo by Ryan Sweeney

Linda Joy (Kennedy) Sweeney lives in Rutland, Massachusetts, with her husband, Kenneth. They have two adult sons.

Linda graduated from Wachusett Regional High School in Holden, Massachusetts. She studied for a year at Ward School of Business in Worcester, Massachusetts. She then began her career in office work at several business locations, including Paul Revere Life Insurance, Assumption College, and the Devereau Foundation. She was employed for several years with the Massachusetts Public Health Department at Rutland Heights Hospital. She then was employed at Worcester State University and retired after eighteen years in several college departments, including personnel, student affairs, and urban studies.

Linda enjoys cooking, gardening, singing, sewing, and crafts projects, especially making primitive dolls.

She was inspired to write Backyard Friends while sitting in her yard one late afternoon watching birds and squirrels playing.

Lightning Source UK Ltd.
Milton Keynes UK
UKRC031032051021
391706UK00001B/4